The Dog and His Reflection

An imprint of Om Books International

A hungry dog once happened to get his paws on a piece of meat in a jungle. He was very happy with the discovery.

But he realised that there were other animals in the jungle who could steal the meat from him as they were more powerful.

"Oh, what should I do now?" the dog wondered worriedly. "How do I protect my food?"

"I know! Let me take this meat home to my village so that I can eat it in peace!" the dog decided and ran through the jungle with the piece of meat in his mouth.

The jungle was separated from the dog's village by a small, running brook. A wooden plank served as the bridge to cross this brook. The dog reached this brook speedily, stepped on the plank carefully with the piece of meat still in his mouth and started crossing the brook slowly.

But something in the water made him stop in his tracks as he was halfway across the makeshift bridge. "Hey, what's that?" the dog thought to himself in surprise. He stopped to stare down at something in the water of the brook.

"There's another dog in the water! He's holding a piece of meat in his mouth that is even bigger than the piece of meat I have!" the dog realised with envy.

Actually, the dog in the water was nothing, but the dog's own shadow that was reflected in the water of the brook below him. But the foolish dog did not know what a shadow was! So he mistook his own shadow to be another dog!

"That's another dog with a piece of meat in his mouth!" he concluded. The dog was very hungry by now and thought to himself, "I'm so hungry! Another piece of meat will be most welcome! "

He continued, "All I have to do is snatch the piece of meat from the dog below in the water. Then, I'll have two pieces of meat instead of one! That should be easy! I'll just scare him away!"

The greedy, stupid dog grabbed at his own shadow in the water to take the imaginary piece of meat, mistaking it to be another dog. He tried to take the meat away from the 'other' dog.

In his excitement, he also barked at the dog in the water, hoping to scare him away.

But no sooner had he done that, than the piece of meat he had been holding in his mouth fell off into the waters of the brook. Splash!

"Oh no! I've lost my piece of meat!" the dog exclaimed sadly. He watched helplessly as the piece of meat sank into the water, never to be seen again.

The dog had lost the meat he had got with so much difficulty only because of his foolishness. As the piece of meat slowly sank in the water the foolish dog saw that the meat in the mouth of the 'dog' in the water had also disappeared!